ADULT SKILLS Literacy for Living

Punctuation - Book 1

Written by Dr Nancy Mills and Dr Graham Lawler

The Adult Skills Range

The range of Adult Skills resources has been developed by Aber Education in response to needs expressed by tutors, students and governmental agencies. The materials are appropriate for adults who require support in advancing their literacy and numeracy skills.

Dr Nancy Mills, Adult Literacy/Numeracy author and editor, has over 25 years of combined experience in the adult education areas of teaching, tutor training, developing curriculum resources and publishing. Dr Graham Lawler, Adult Literacy/Numeracy author and editor, has over 27 years of combined experience in the adult education areas of teaching, tutor training, developing curriculum resources and publishing.

Adult Skills - Punctuation - Book 1

ISBN 978-1-84285-110-4

© 2009 Aber Publishing

P.O. Box 225

Abergele

Conwy County LL18 9AY

Published in Europe by Aber Publishing. www.aber-publishing.co.uk

Cover illustration by Michelle Cooper

Typesetting by Angela Grryp and Aber Publishing

Contents

Introduction

General

This resource deals with the use and application of basic punctuation. It has been written to provide:

- a progression of punctuation skills,
- exercises for practising and developing punctuation skills,
- summary pages for revision and reference,
- blackline masters for multiple use.

Tutor knowledge of these skills is essential so that you can provide students with:

- focus and goals,
- quality modelling sessions,
- quality feedback,
- quality practice,
- purposeful conferencing,
- pre- and post-evaluation.

This resource can be used for:

- individual or small group lessons,
- individual practice and revision,
- take home practice.

Lessons can be used:

- in the sequence they appear in the book,
- as starters for a focus on one of the skills,
- to collect baseline information for individual students,
- as pre- or post-tests, before or after the study of a particular skill.

These skills facilitate the development of:

- reading,
- writing,
- self-confidence in putting pen to paper.

Using this resource

What is punctuation? – pages 1-2

Before launching into activity sheets on punctuation marks, it is important that students understand the purposes and uses of punctuation. If they don't know the term punctuation, they will certainly recognise some of the punctuation marks. The first step is to ensure that they relate the word punctuation to the various marks.

A discussion of the purpose of punctation in general, with spoken or written examples, is relevant at this point. "Why punctuate?" "How does punctuation help us understand what we read?"

Once they have grasped the general concept of punctuation, ask them to think of all the punctuation marks they can and put one in each bubble (page 1). If they have trouble, you may give them some text and ask them to find some marks to copy into the bubbles. If they don't get them all, you may show them the ones they have missed so that they can fill in all the bubbles:

.   C   ?   !   ,   " "   '

Ask questions so that you can determine if they have understood the importance of punctuation marks and are ready to move to their use.

At the completion of this discussion give them a copy of page 2.
Work with each student as they fill in the blanks.

Punctuation – summary – page 3

This page has been included as a summary sheet or for use as a wall chart. It could be used:
- after the activity to reinforce the concept,
- after the punctuation pages and the 'What is punctuation?' discussion have been completed.

Note: This resouce includes a summary for each of the seven punctuation marks introduced. They can all be used as described above.

What is a sentence? – page 4

This page is helpful to solicit the students' understanding of sentences. If working in a small group, their ideas can be shared, accepted and returned to after the sentence sheets have been completed. The activity can be used as a pre- and post-test to gauge student progress.

Capital letters and fullstops and practice – pages 5-7

Use these three pages to review the concept of a complete sentence and reinforce the use of capital letters and fullstops.

The exercises can be used:
- as a one-on-one or small group exercise for general discussion. Is each one a sentence? If so, why? If not, why not?,
- as a follow-up exercise for revision,
- to correct the punctuation by putting in the capital letter or a fullstop, or both,
- to complete the idea to make it a sentence.

After the student has ticked the complete sentences, the activities may be used again by the students to make the other sentences complete.

More about capital letters, and practice – pages 8-9

The purpose of these pages is to give examples of additional uses of capital letters. The activities will help to reinforce the use of all three concepts that have been introduced:
- complete sentences,
- fullstops,
- capital letters.

Capital letters and fullstops – punctuating a story – page 10

This page has stories with no punctuation marks. Ask students to make corrections to any or all of the stories. These can be used as a one-on-one or small group activity. They provide an opportunity for students to discuss where and why sentences begin or end in certain places and to justify their ideas. The groups can be of mixed or similar ability.
The summary (page 11) can be used in the same ways as suggested for page 3.

Joined sentences – page 12

Before students fully understand sentence structure and punctuation, their writing may be full of joined ideas using and and then. Joining sentences in this way is easier than forming new sentences. Use this page with students to improve their writing.

Question marks and exclamation marks – page 13-15

The purpose of these pages is to get students thinking about other punctuation marks used in sentences and the reasons for their use.

As part of the activity, they could either write a sentence that requires a ! or a ?, or find an example in a book or story you provide.

The activities give practice in recognising and using question marks and exclamation marks.

The summary (page 16) can be used in the same ways as suggested for page 3.

Speech marks – pages 17-18

These pages have been developed to provide a staged introduction to punctuating with speech marks:

- Examples of why speech marks are used are presented. There is also an activity that requires students to underline the spoken parts of a fully punctuated sentence.

- The idea of beginning each new speaker on a new line is introduced.

- Conversations are provided for the students to read and answer questions that require an understanding of the punctuation.

Commas used with speech marks – pages 19-21

The rest of the activities deal with the other punctuation involved in speaking and the placement of . ! ? ,. There are also conversations for students to write and punctuate.

The summary (page 22) can be used in the same ways as suggested for page 3.

Commas – other uses – page 23

This section introduces the placement of commas in lists of nouns and describing words, and to indicate a pause in the reading. The exercises will reinforce this use of commas. The summary (page 24) can be used in the same way as page 3.

Apostrophes – missing letters – pages 25-27

These pages deal with apostrophes in shortened words. This concept is usually logical to students and easy to grasp. There are many practice activities.

Apostrophes – possession – page 28

The placement of possessive apostrophes is more difficult. It is a tricky concept and one that people of all ages find hard to use properly. Mastery will need time, revision and practice.

Examples and activities will help to reinforce this concept. The summary (page 29) can be used in the same ways as suggested for page 3.

Punctuation practice – pages 30-33

Here are some revision activities for all the punctuation marks. They can also be used as a pre- or post-test. An answer key for the activities on page 32 is on page 33.

© 2009 Aber Publishing – Adult Skills   Punctuation - Book 1

What is punctuation?

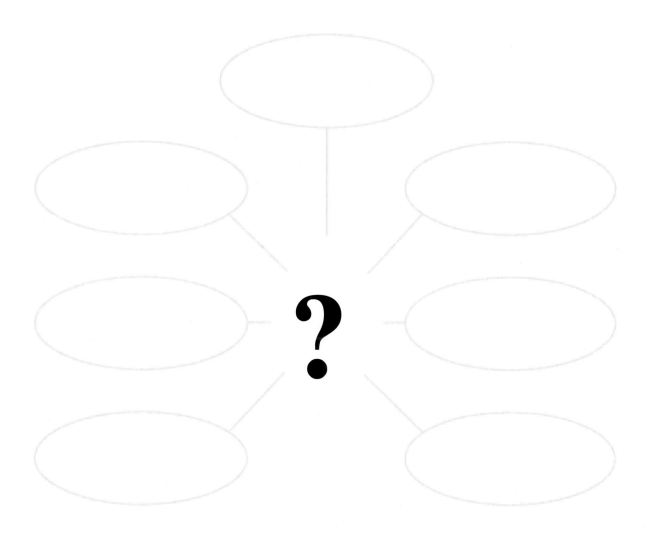

What is punctuation?

What do we mean by **punctuation?**

Punctuation is . . .

Activity

Fill in the gaps below by putting in the punctuation mark.

	A fullstop is a mark that shows the end of a sentence.
	A capital letter goes at the beginning of a sentence.
	A question mark shows a question has been asked.
	An exclamation mark shows surprise, excitement or anger.
	Speech marks show something is being said.
	A comma is used for a pause in a sentence. It is also used to separate items in a list.
	An apostrophe is used to show where letters have been taken out of a word. It is also used to show ownership.

Punctuation summary

L M N W

Capital Letters

- at the beginning of sentences
- at the beginning of names of people and places
- the word **I**

Fullstop

- at the end of a sentence

!

Exclamation Mark

- at the end of a sentence to show surprise, alarm, anger

?

Question Mark

- at the end of a question

9 or ,

Comma

- for a pause in a sentence
- between words in a list of things

66 99 or 66 99

Speech Marks

- to show spoken words

9 or

Apostrophes

- when letters have been left out to shorten a word
- when ownership needs to be shown

What is a sentence?

We know that **punctuation** is a group of special marks used in sentences. They make sentences easier to understand.

What is a sentence?

A sentence is a group of words or an idea which makes sense on its own.
All sentences have punctuation marks; a capital letter at the beginning and a fullstop at the end.

I have a dog.	**This is a complete sentence.** **It makes sense and has a punctuation mark.**
Come over here.	**This is a complete sentence because it makes sense.**
If you want to.	**This is not a complete sentence. It has a punctuation mark, but it does not make sense.**

Activity

Put a ✓ in the boxes:

- if you think it is a complete sentence,
- if it has punctuation,
- if it does not make sense.

	complete sentence	has punctuation	does not make sense
I have a dog and	☐	☐	☐
Today I am going to the movies.	☐	☐	☐
My car is.	☐	☐	☐
It rained all day.	☐	☐	☐
Tomorrow is my birthday.	☐	☐	☐
Last weekend we climbed the	☐	☐	☐
I went shopping with.	☐	☐	☐
My job interview is on Friday.	☐	☐	☐
The team will stay in	☐	☐	☐
We are having chicken for tea	☐	☐	☐
Let me know when you get home.	☐	☐	☐
My brother is going to the London to.	☐	☐	☐
Scott's wedding is going to be.	☐	☐	☐

Capital letters and fullstops

A sentence needs three things to make it complete:

* It must make sense.
* It must start with a capital letter.
* It must end with a fullstop.

C	**capital letter**	All sentences must begin with a **capital letter**.
.	**full stop**	A **fullstop** is a punctuation mark that shows the end of a sentence.

I drove to town.	**This is a complete sentence.**
I don't think I.	**This is not a sentence. It has a fullstop and a capital letter, but it does not make sense.**
i like reading	**This is a sentence but it needs a capital letter and a fullstop to complete it.**

Activity

Are these complete sentences?

Put a ✓ in the boxes:

* if you think it is a complete sentence,
* if it has a fullstop,
* if it starts with a capital letter,
* if it does not make sense.

	complete sentence	has a fullstop	starts with a capital letter	does not make sense
We played cricket on Saturday.	☐	☐	☐	☐
In the holidays to the Wales	☐	☐	☐	☐
my cat just had kittens.	☐	☐	☐	☐
the two cars crashed at the.	☐	☐	☐	☐
I went to the fireworks display last.	☐	☐	☐	☐
You can sit down.	☐	☐	☐	☐
let's go swimming in the river.	☐	☐	☐	☐
The road by my house is all torn up	☐	☐	☐	☐
in the morning I have to go to work.	☐	☐	☐	☐
Every Friday I go out with.	☐	☐	☐	☐

Capital letters and full stops – practice

Are these sentences? Does each one begin with a **capital letter** and end with a **fullstop**?

I am going to work today.	Yes! This sentence begins with a capital letter and ends with a fullstop. It is a complete sentence.
Mike works in a shop.	Yes! This sentence begins with a capital letter and ends with a fullstop. It is a complete sentence.
Going to work today. I start work at.	No! These are NOT complete sentences. They have capital letters and fullstops, but they do not make sense.
today is Sunday.	No! This is a sentence but it needs a capital letter to complete it.
I will work until 8	No! This is a sentence but it needs a fullstop to complete it.

Activity

Are these complete sentences?

Put a ✓ in the boxes:

- if you think it is a complete sentence,
- if it has a fullstop,
- if it starts with a capital letter,
- if it does not make sense.

	complete sentence	has a fullstop	starts with a capital letter	does not make sense
My name is Mike.	☐	☐	☐	☐
I have a job at.	☐	☐	☐	☐
I walk to.	☐	☐	☐	☐
I get to work about 8.	☐	☐	☐	☐
Sometimes I put things on the shelves	☐	☐	☐	☐
Most of the time I sell things.	☐	☐	☐	☐
I work until.	☐	☐	☐	☐
Then	☐	☐	☐	☐
I get home at 9 pm	☐	☐	☐	☐
on Fridays I get paid.	☐	☐	☐	☐

Capital letters and fullstops – practice

Activities

Put a capital letter at the beginning of each complete sentence.

Put a fullstop at the end of each complete sentence.

When you are finished, put a ✓ next to each complete sentence.

Story 1

i have to work on weekends

i get paid each

my mate and I work together

the shop is near my house

birmingham is the city where I

lots of people come into the shop

the shop closes at

we sell food and drinks

when we close

sometimes I walk to work with

i go home after the shop closes

Story 2

my sister and I were invited to the bach

it was about 5 kilometres

the shop was near Lake Windermere

when we arrived, the first thing we did

there were three bedrooms

we put our things on one of the

seven others arrived shortly after

there were only six beds

each person put their things on a bed

everyone had chosen a bed to

my sister and i had put our things on one bed

so my sister and i had to sleep

© 2009 Aber Publishing – Adult Skills   Punctuation - Book 1

More about capital letters

You know that **all** sentences begin with a **capital letter**.

Capitals are also used in other ways.

Names of people..................... begin with **capital letters**. .... John Wayne, Mrs Jones

Names of places .... begin with **capital letters**. .... Cardiff, Wales
.... Edinburgh University

Names of days....................... begin with **capital letters**. .... Monday, Friday

Names of months   begin with **capital letters** .... July, December

Names given.. to other things................. begin with **capital letters** Titanic, The Sting
.... Toyota, Yellow Pages

Names of streets.................... begin with **capital letters**. .... Main Street, M1 Motorway

Names of businesses .... begin with **capital letters** .... Burger King, Qantas

I... **I** is always a **capital letter**.............. I work in a shop.

We work in a shop.	**This sentence begins with a capital letter.**
My name is Mike Hall.	**Names of people begin with capital letters.**
London is the capital of the U.K.	**Names of places begin with capital letters.**
Saturday and Sunday are busy days.	**Names of days begin with capital letters.**
I am reading a book called Lord of the Rings.	**Titles of books begin with capital letters.**
My brother just bought a Toyota.	**Names of cars begin with capital letters.**
Sometimes I pump petrol.	**I by itself is always a capital letter.**

Activity

Read these sentences.

Circle all the capital letters that are correct.

Cross out the capital letters that are wrong and write in the correct letter.

My job is Fun.

I work Monday through Friday.

The Boss is nice.

My Mate jay works with Me.

I am enjoying the book called the great escape.

jodie drives an old honda.

i work in Leicester.

Capital letters – practice

Activity

Correct the capital letters in these sentences.

Put a fullstop at the end of each complete sentence.

If it is not complete, finish the sentence and put in a fullstop.

we ate at macdonalds

i am flying on virgin airlines

a band called which way is up is coming to

they are working on high street

my interview is with the bank of ireland

my birthday is in october

mr Wilson is in loughborough hospital

the listener is my favourite

wellington is the capital of new

on wednesday i will play tennis

we are all going to meet at halfmoon bay café

the movie we are going to see is called the last samurai

he went to australia and saw the opera house

mr clark asked me to work overtime on saturday

the coalville netball club is looking for new players

please buy me a copy of next magazine at the corner shop

my neice is going to the somerset college of arts and technology

the plymouth public library is not open on sundays

in san francisco i went over the golden gate bridge

the wales rugby team are playing in south africa next weekend

my favourite biscuits are on sale at the local asda supermarket

the golf tournament will be held at seaside golf course in abergele

my brother got a new apple computer at work

she lives on state highway 1

i am going to name my new puppy duke

Capital letters and fullstops – punctuating a story

Activities

These stories make no sense because they have no punctuation.

There are no capital letters or fullstops.

Put in the correct punctuation so that the stories make sense.

Story 1

mike hall works in a shop the shop is in wellington he usually works on weekends mike walks to work if the weather is fine if it is very cold he rides a bus payday is on fridays mike's mates john and sally also work at the shop after work john and mike are going to sally's party

Story 2

this saturday i am going rock climbing with my mate he has all the equipment he is going to teach me to use it i will put on all the safety gear we will start at an easy place if i am good at it we will try a harder area i am really looking forward to learning to rock climb

Story 3

my sister is getting married my mother and i went with her to choose a wedding dress it is white with tiny pearls around the neck i will be a bridesmaid in the wedding my dress will be light blue all the bridesmaids will carry white and pink flowers it will be a beautiful wedding

Story 4

my father is a carpenter he builds houses on monday i had a day off work so i went to work with him i thought i might want to become a carpenter too first we stopped by the shop and bought a large box of nails then we stopped at a dairy and bought some food for lunch during the day i spent a lot of time hammering in nails by the time we went home my arm was aching i think i will keep my job

Capital letters – summary

Capital letters are used:

- **at the beginning of a sentence**

  Tomorrow it will rain.

- **for the names of people and places**

  Tom, Mrs Miller, Llandudno, Wales

- **for the names of streets and buildings**

  Devon Road, Xerox House, M25, TSB Building

- **for the days of the week and months of the year**

  Monday, January

- **for the word I**

  Mary and I are meeting for lunch.

- **at the beginning of speaking**

  She said, "What a pretty cat."

- **for special days**

  Christmas, Labour Day, Queen's Birthday

- **for titles**

  The Bible

  Lord of the Rings

© 2009 Aber Publishing – Adult Skills   Punctuation - Book 1

Joined sentences

Sometimes when we write we forget about what makes sentences complete. We may write several ideas that are joined together with words like **then** or **and**. These sentences can get very long and need extra punctuation.

Activities

Here are examples of stories that have a lot of <u>ands</u> and <u>thens</u> joining ideas together.

Improve the story by crossing out each unwanted <u>and</u> and <u>then</u>.

Put in any missing capital letters and fullstops.

Story 1

On friday john and i went to sally's party after work and we talked to some of her friends and had something to eat then we got tired because we worked all day and then we found someone to take us home because it was too late to catch a bus and when we got home there was a good movie on TV and we were not tired anymore and we made popcorn and watched the movie then we fell asleep on the couch and in the morning laughed at ourselves and our wrinkled clothing that we slept in and then changed clothes and went to work.

Story 2

i got my first skateboard when i was ten and decided that i wanted to be a champion skateboarder and i started practising every day and then when i was 18 i entered my first competition in my age group and won second place and it was so exciting and then when i was 22 i entered the skateboard championships in london and there were skateboarders from all over the world then i practised more than ever and ended up winning the competition and also a trip to the world skateboard championships in los angeles california and i didn't get a place but it was great meeting all the other competitors and having a trip overseas

Story 3

it was our last netball game of the season and my team was tied for first place in our league and there were 8 people from work on the team but they needed a substitution and even though i had never played netball before i had watched it and knew the rules and they asked me to play so i said i would and on the night of the game i was so nervous and sat on the bench for the first three quarters but in the last quarter one of the girls sprained her ankle and another was very tired so then they put me in and to make a long story short we ended up winning by two points and i was so glad that i had played a small part in it

Question marks and exclamation marks

You have learned that a sentence starts with a capital letter. It ends with a fullstop.

There are two other punctuation marks that a sentence can end with.

Like a fullstop, they show that a sentence has ended but they carry more meaning than a fullstop.

Why use these punctuation marks to end a sentence?

• I need to go to the supermarket.	Use a fullstop to show the end of a sentence.
? How long have you been working at the shop?	Use a question mark to show that a question has been asked.
! Someone tried to rob me last night!	Use an exclamation mark to show something has been shouted, said strongly or in surprise.
Ouch! I think I just broke my toe!	

Activities

1. **Read each sentence. If you think it asks a question, turn the fullstop into a question mark.**

    Lots of people are going to Sally's party.

    What time are you going to arrive.

    John and I are going together.

    Will Sally have some food.

    How late are you working tomorrow.

    I have to take the cash to the bank before the party.

    When will you leave the party.

2. **Read each sentence. If you think it has been shouted, said strongly or in surprise, change the fullstop to an exclamation mark.**

    My father went to the bank to deposit some money.

    He noticed a man grabbing a bag from the clerk at the next counter.

    The man ran out of the bank.

    My father took off in pursuit.

    He chased the robber for about four blocks.

    Police cars started appearing.

    They took over the chase and caught the robber.

    The next day my father got his photograph in the paper.

Question marks and exclamation marks

3. **Read each sentence. If you think a fullstop is wrong, change it to a question mark or exclamation mark.**

Last night we went to the car races.

Wasn't it excellent.

There were thousands of people there.

Did you see lots of people you knew.

During the first race one of the cars crashed into the wall.

The ambulance came to get the driver but he was OK.

Everything was pretty quiet for the next three races.

Did you see the driver in the last race lose control.

Two of the cars got by him safely.

The next thing we knew, there were about eight cars piled up.

Two ambulances and lots of people rushed to help the drivers.

The noise was deafening and there was smoke everywhere.

They ended up cancelling the last race.

There were only two cars left running.

Do you want to go to races again next Saturday.

4. **Read each sentence. Add fullstops, question marks and exclamation marks.**

What time are you leaving on the plane

I am supposed to be at the airport by 4:00 to check in

Do you know what time it is

Oh no, it is 3:00

Have you packed yet

No, I haven't

How long will it take you to drive to the airport

At least half an hour

I think you are going to miss your plane

I can't miss it

Then why are we still here talking about it

Get going

Question marks and exclamation marks

Activities

1. **Read this story. Circle the question marks that are used correctly.**

    Cross out the question marks that are not used correctly and put in a fullstop.

    Do you know where I work?

    I work at a shop in London?

    My boss wants me to work this weekend?

    I can't work because my parents are coming to visit me?

    Will they stay in your flat?

    What will you fix them for dinner?

    They are leaving on Sunday night?

2. **Read these sentences. If you think they have been shouted, said strongly or in surprise, put in an exclamation mark. If not, put in a fullstop.**

    The shop where I work was robbed

    Across from the shop is the bank

    Mike is taking the cash to the bank

    Hurry up, Mike, someone is following you

    Mike is running towards the bank

    Mike is safely in the bank

    He is on his way back to the shop now

    Mike said he was very scared when that person was following him

3. **Put in a question mark, exclamation mark or fullstop where it belongs.**

    Did you ring the police

    The price of petrol has gone up

    Jake got fired

    Don't touch the alarm button or it will go off

    My mate Sally broke her arm when she fell off the ladder

    Is London in England

    There were over a hundred people at Mike's party

    What time did the last person leave

    How did you get home

    I was going to take the bus

    Stop, I yelled, as it left without me

Fullstops, question marks and exclamation marks – summary

A **sentence** is a word, or group of words, which makes sense on its own.

A **punctuation mark** is at the end of each sentence.

•

Fullstop

My name is Mike.

It is Tuesday.

Yesterday it rained.

?

Question mark

What time does the movie start?

Where are my glasses?

When is her birthday?

!

Exclamation mark

Watch out for that truck!

The smoke alarm really scared me!

I can't believe I won the election!

Speech marks

Speech marks are sometimes called **quotation marks**.
They are always at the beginning and end of what the person said.

Why do we use speech marks?
In many stories there are people who speak. Speech marks go around spoken words. We use them to show the exact words that have been said.

Mike said he was going to walk home after the party.	These words are NOT said.
"I had to walk home after the party," said Mike.	This sentence shows what words are said.
Mary said that she would meet me at the party.	These words are NOT said.
Mary said, "I will meet you at the party."	This sentence shows what words are said.

Activity

In the story below, Mike and John are speaking to each other.

When they are speaking, underline the words that they say like this:

"<u>I am going to apply for another job</u>," Mike told John.

"I am going to apply for another job," Mike told John.

"Don't tell the boss," he said.

"I won't," agreed Mike.

"You should apply at the dairy by your house," suggested John.

Mike replied, "I have a friend who told me about a job at the supermarket."

"That's great," said John. "Do you have an interview?"

"Yes," answered Mike. "It's tomorrow morning at 9."

"But you have to start work at 8," warned John.

"I know. I'm going to tell Mrs James I will be late," explained Mike.

Circle all the speech marks.

Notice that they should be at the beginning and the end of the underlines you drew.

© 2009 Aber Publishing – Adult Skills   Punctuation - Book 1

Speech marks

Activities

1. **In this story, Mike and Sally are speaking to each other. Notice that each new person's words start on a new line.**

   Underline what Mike says. Put a circle around what Sally says.

   "I had an interview for a job at the supermarket," Mike told Sally.

   "That's great, Mike," Sally replied. "Did you get the job?"

   "I don't know yet," he answered. "They will tell me tomorrow."

   "How much do they pay per hour?" asked Sally.

   "They start at £6.00. They will review it in three months," explained Mike.

2. **In this story, some people are talking to each other. Read it first, then answer the questions below. Underline each person's spoken words.**

   "My boyfriend and I went down to the beach last night," Sally told John. "We walked along the shore for about an hour."

   "Wasn't it cold?" inquired John.

   "It wasn't too bad until he tried to throw me in!" complained Sally.

   "Did you get all wet?" laughed John.

   "No, I was able to get away from him," Sally explained. "I don't think he really would have pushed me in," Sally admitted.

   a) How many people are speaking? _____

   b) Who is asking all the questions? _____

   c) Why was an exclamation mark used in Sally's speech? _____

   d) What was the answer to the first question? _____

   e) What was John doing when he said, "Did you get all wet?" _____

3. **In this story, the speech marks have been left out.**
   Put them where they belong.

   Do you want to go kayaking my brother and me? asked Trudy.

   I've never been before, Karl admitted.

   That doesn't matter. It's easy, Trudy explained.

   I'll probably fall overboard! exclaimed Karl. I'm not very coordinated.

   Can you swim? inquired Trudy.

   Yes, I learned to swim when I was 5, boasted Karl.

   Then even if you fall overboard you won't drown, Trudy replied. Besides, we always wear life jackets.

   Karl was excited. He said I'd love to come! Thanks for inviting me.

Commas used with speech marks

Use a comma after the words have been said, before the speech marks.

"I am going to the beach," said Matthew.	In this sentence, "I am going to the beach," is what Matthew actually said.
	We are writing down what Matthew said and adding said Matthew to the sentence.
	Put a comma after the speaking.
	Put a fullstop at the end of the complete sentence.
Matthew said he was going to the beach.	**Speech marks are NOT used in this sentence. We have not written Matthew's actual words.**

Use a comma after the speaker is mentioned and before the words that have been   spoken.

Jenny whispered, "Don't tell her."	**In this sentence, the speaker is mentioned first. We are writing what Jenny actually <u>whispered</u> and adding <u>Jenny</u> whispered to the sentence.**
	Put a comma after the speaker.
	Put a capital letter at the beginning of the speaking.
	Put a fullstop at the end of the complete sentence.
Jenny whispered not to tell her.	**Speech marks are NOT used in this sentence. We have not written Jenny's actual words.**

Activity
Put fullstops and commas in the right places in these sentences.

"Be sure to lock your car" Susan said

Mr Miller requested "I'd like change for five pounds"

The farmer told his wife he would be late for lunch

Jerry whispered "I'm going to look for another job"

Colin told me that the movie would start at 6pm

"Don't forget we're meeting Mum for lunch" his sister reminded

© 2009 Aber Publishing – Adult Skills   Punctuation - Book 1

Commas used with speech marks

When the speaking is a question, or is said strongly, shouted, or in surprise, put in a question mark or exclamation mark after the words are spoken.

"What time is it?" asked Nick.	**In this sentence the ? is put right after the question.**
"Stop!" shouted the man.	**In this sentence, the ! is put right after what the man shouted.**

Activity

Put fullstops, commas, question marks and exclamation marks in the right places in these sentences.

Susan shouted "Watch out for that car"

Mr Miller requested "Could I have change for five pounds"

The farmer reported to his wife "My tractor is broken again"

"Are you going to look for another job" Jerry asked

"Have you forgotten that we are meeting friends for lunch" she queried

"Are you going horseback riding this weekend" asked Tina

"Halt" demanded the policeman

The singer asked "Would you like me to sing your favourite song"

"Did you buy yourself a new surfboard" inquired Susan

My father warned "Don't touch that fence. The wires are live"

"An accident has happened at the end of the street" she yelled

My boss asked "Can you work late on Friday"

"There will be severe thunder storms tonight" the weather presenter announced

"Are you going to the big sale in town" Jude asked

Gary pointed "You've left your car windows open"

The clerk inquired "How much do you want to spend"

"When is my new desk arriving" I asked the manager

"A large earthquake has hit Japan and caused many deaths" reported the radio host

A conversation

Activities

Study these pictures. Give each person a name and write down what you think they are saying to each other.

Put in all the correct punctuation   .   ?   !   ,   " "

1.

2.

66 99

When we write down what several people say, each person's speaking is on a new line.

"That was a good meal," Robin commented.

"I agree. I especially liked the soup," replied Don.

Robin continued, "I didn't have the soup, but the mussels were great."

Don suggested, "Let's eat here again soon."

66 99

Speech marks go at the beginning and end of what the person said.

Use a comma after the words have been said.

"Please ring if you're going to be late," Janes mother reminded her.

Use a comma after the speaker is mentioned.

Morgan pleaded, "Will you work for me on Saturday night?"

Other punctuation used in spoken sentences:

?

Question mark

"Do you want to go to the movies on Friday night?" Brad invited me.

"No, I have to work late," Paula replied.

"How about Saturday night?" Brad persisted.

"Sure. What time will you collect me?" Paula asked.

Brad thought for a minute and said, "I'll be at your house at 7."

!

Exclamation mark

Mary cried, "I just broke my new coffee mug!"

"Watch out! Don't step on any of the pieces," said Sam.

"Ouch!" said Nick as he walked into the kitchen. "I think I've cut my foot!"

"Put some pressure on the cut and I'll get a plaster," volunteered Mary.

Commas – other uses

Commas are used in speaking to separate what is said from who said it.

There is another use for commas.

I bought bread, cheese and milk.	**A comma is used to separate items in a list of things.** **Don't put a comma before the word <u>and</u>.**
I looked out over the clear, warm, blue water.	**Commas are also used in lists of describing words.**

Activities

1. Put the commas in these lists of things.

On his trip, Rich is going to London Reading and Cardiff

Rich packed his shoes socks pants and shirts.

When Rich arrives in London he is going to go to Big Ben, the art museum Parliament and the river.

Rich is travelling with Grant Lisa Cindy and Bill.

2. Put the commas in these lists of describing words.

The skiers came down the steep icy slopes.

We were hot tired and sandy after a day at the beach.

His gumboots were brown muddy and heavy after walking across the paddock.

One more way a comma is used is to mark a place in a sentence to make you pause.

3. Read this sentence out loud. When you come to the comma, stop reading briefly.

When you get home, would you feed the dog?

It should have felt comfortable for you to slow down or pause when you came to the comma.

Fill in the commas in these sentences where there is a pause.

When I get up   I shower and shave before breakfast.

After the movie   we are going out to eat.

Mick got injured in the rugby match   but he will be able to play next week.

No matter what happens   call me when you get home.

If you want to take Steph to the party   you had better ring her.

Comma – summary

Commas are used:

,

- **to separate what is said from who said it**

"I am going to work now," said Mike.

Mike said, "I am going to work now."

,

- **to separate items in a list**

I need to wash my shirts, socks and underwear.

We will stop in London, Taunton, Plymouth and Cardiff.

"Can you stop by the store and get milk, eggs, bread and a tomato?"

,

- **in lists of describing words**

From the plane I saw tall, white mountains.

"I have never eaten such a yummy, huge, delicious ice-cream before."

,

- **to mark a place in a sentence to make you pause**

When you finish eating, please clean your dishes.

On Saturday morning, the neighbour boy will cut our grass.

Apostrophes – missing letters

There are two ways to use apostrophes.

One way to use an apostrophe is

• to shorten or abbreviate words - an apostrophe takes the place of the missing letters.

Here is how the apostrophe is used to shorten or abbreviate words:

is not   isn't   I am   I'm

Shorten the two words to one by taking out one or two letters.

The apostrophe is put in to show where the letters have been taken out.

Use the apostrophe to show that a letter has been left out of the word.

I do not think Jack has arrived yet. I don't think Jack has arrived yet.	The o in do not has been left out. An apostrophe has been put in where the o was taken out.
He is going to work all night. He's going to work all night.	These two sentences have the same meaning. The i in is has been left out. An apostrophe has been put in where the i was taken out.

Activity

Look at the two words on the left of each box.

Then look at the shortened words on the right.

Put a circle around the letters on the left that have been left out of each word on the right.

Put the apostrophe in each word on the right where the letters have been taken out.

I have	I ve		do not	don t
we will	we ll		I am	I m
I would	I d		is not	isn t
have not	haven t		has not	hasn t
let us	let s		can not	can t
Owen is	Owen s		I have	I ve
I will	I ll		she is	she s

Apostrophes – missing letters

Activities

1. **In these sentences, cross out the bold words and write in one word with an apostrophe.**

   I have _____ been waiting to get a car for a year.

   We will _____ arrive at about 8.

   I would _____ like to get my haircut tomorrow.

   I have not _____ deposited my pay cheque at the bank.

   Let us _____ go to see the new band when it comes to town.

   Kiley is _____ meeting his friend at the train station.

   I will _____ make cheese muffins for my parents when they come to visit.

   Do not _____ burn yourself on the stove.

   I am _____ taking my driving exam next week.

   This is not _____ the right time to change jobs.

   She has not _____ told me when to pick her up.

   He can not _____ remember to pay the docket.

   I have _____ decided to move to Scotland if I can find a job.

2. **Fill in the words in each blank that mean the same as the bold word on the right.**

   _____**Don't** forget my birthday.

   _____You **haven't** filled in your time sheet.

   _____We **can't** have lunch at the train station.

   _____It **wouldn't** be right if he was promoted before me.

   _____We **shouldn't** go camping until it gets warmer.

   _____Mrs James **doesn't** know where Judy has gone.

   The same word has been shortened in each word. What is it? _____

3. **Fill in the words on each line that mean the same as the bold word on the right.**

   _____**I'll** be home late tonight.

   _____**She'll** get the groceries before she comes home.

   _____**We'll** take the television into the repair shop.

   _____**He'll** never know who ran into his car in the carpark.

   _____**They'll** have to buy their tickets soon.

   The same word has been shortened in each word. What is it? _____

Apostrophes – missing letters

4. **Fill in the words on each line that mean the same as the bold word on the right.**

_____**I've** made a booking for the restaurant.

_____**They've** paid for their petrol.

_____**We've** decided that we will all wear black to the party.

_____We **should've** have all turned out the lights when we left.

The same word has been shortened in each word. What is it? _____

5. **Fill in the words on each line that mean the same as the bold word on the right.**

_____ **She's** going home now.

_____ **Jan's** shifting flats this weekend.

_____ **He's** washing his car.

_____ **Mike's** enrolled in a computer course.

_____ Mr **Hill's** opening a new shop.

_____ **It's** a good day to walk on the beach.

The same word has been shortened in each word. What is it? _____

6. **Fill in the words on each line that mean the same as the bold word on the right.**

_____**I'm** going out with Bill tomorrow night.

_____ **Let's** meet in town for lunch on Friday.

_____ **We'd** better hurry or we will get caught in the rain.

_____ **He'd** look good with a haircut.

7. **Fill in each gap with a word that has an apostrophe.**

As soon as you turn the corner _____ see my flat.

Please _____ let the dog get out the gate.

On Saturday _____ going to the craft fair.

She _____ have been late if she had left earlier.

_____ leaving for Birmingham in the morning.

_____ that your dad who waved to us?

_____ going to be arriving at the station soon.

If _____ not here by 7 _____ leave without them.

_____ let you stay in our flat while _____ gone.

_____ anyone going to answer that phone?

© 2009 Aber Publishing – Adult Skills   Punctuation - Book 1

Apostrophes – possession

Another use of **apostrophes** is
• to show that something belongs to something else or to someone.

How do we use apostrophes for possession?

There is the tourist's bag.	**The apostrophe before the s̲ shows that the bags belong to the tourist – one person.**
I think that is Don's dog.	**The apostrophe before the s̲ shows that the dog belongs to Don – one person.**
Those are the players' uniforms.	**The apostrophe after the s̲ shows that the uniforms belong belong to all the players.**
All the musicians' instruments were lost during the flight.	**The apostrophe after the s̲ shows that the instruments belong to all the musicians – more than one person.**

Activity

Look at the pictures and ask yourself, "Who does it belong to?" That question helps you decide where the apostrophe goes.

If it belongs to one person, the apostrophe goes before the s̲.

If it belongs to more than one person, the apostrophe goes after the s̲.

Examples:

There is only one man and one book.
Here is the man's book.

There are several students with books.
Here are the students' books.

1. Put the apostrophes in the correct places.

One person or thing.

This is my friends ring.

Look at that cars wheels.

Listen to Tinas new CD.

Look out for the dogs bite.

The boys shirt got torn when he fell.

More than one person or thing.

These are my friends rings.

Look at those cars wheels.

The CDs covers are all mixed up.

There were dogs everywhere.

The boys shirts got torn when they fell.

Apostrophe – summary

'

- An **apostrophe** is used to shorten two words to make one word.

  do not   don't   I am   I'm

- An **apostrophe** is put in where the letters have been taken out.

'

- An **apostrophe** is used to show that something belongs to something or someone.

The tourist's bags were lost.

The placement of the **apostrophe before** the **s** tells us something belongs to **one** person or thing.

The bags belongs to **one** tourist.

The tourists' bags were lost.

The placement of the **apostrophe after** the **s** tells us something belongs to more than **one** person or thing.

The bags belong to more than **one** tourist.

There is only one man and one book.
Here is the man's book.

There are several students with books.
Here are the students' books.

Punctuation practice

? Use a **question mark** in a sentence that asks a question.

!   Use an **exclamation mark** in a sentence that is said strongly.

. Use a **fullstop** at the end of all other sentences.

1. **Read the sentences below. Decide on the punctuation mark each sentence needs. Put one of the three marks at the end of each sentence.**

   Today we often see trains

   Some people ride them to work or school

   It makes me so mad when I can't find a seat

   Have you taken a train on holidays

   Once I saw a train run into a truck

   It was an awful crash

   Luckily no one was hurt

   Do you know when the first railway was built

   It was in London, nearly 200 years ago

   C   Use a **capital** to start the names of people, places and days.
   The word **I** is always a capital letter.

   .   Use a **fullstop** at the end of a complete sentence.

   ,   Use a **comma** in a sentence to separate lists.

2. **Decide on the punctuation each sentence needs. Put fullstops, commas and capital letters where they should go in the sentences.**

   boats are used for fishing taking people across the water and for fun

   the Isle of Man ferry leaves from llandudno

   the ferry takes people cars trucks and supplies to ireland

   the first luxury car was built by a mr rolls and mr royce

   they had to bring food water and other supplies

   one famous ship was the titanic

   the titanic was a new large expensive ship

   when the titanic sank it lost many passengers and crew

   the story of noah's ark is told in the christian bible

   this boat saved women men children and animals from a large destructive flood

   noah's ark is probably the most famous boat of all

Punctuation practice

> **,** An **apostrophe** is used to show that something belongs to something or someone.

1. Put the apostrophes where they should go in the sentences.

The bus drivers training day for all the new employees is next Friday.

The cars tyre has a puncture.

When are the travellers passports going to be ready?

After lunch we're going to Sarahs house.

Will you make the babys bed after you get him up?

> **" "** Use **speech marks** around the words someone says.
>
> **,** Use an **apostrophe** to show a letter has been left out of a word.
>
> **,** Use **commas** to separate what is said from who said it.

2. Decide on the punctuation marks each sentence needs.
   Put speech marks where they should go in the sentences.
   Change the bold words so that they have an apostrophe.
   (The first one is done for you.)

My mate didn't (**did not**) have a car.

He asked Do you know anyone who wants to sell a car

No I (**do not**) _____ I said

Will you go with me to look for one   he asked

I (**can not**) _____ , I admitted. But you (**should not**) _____ go alone.

Why not he inquired

(**It is**) _____ better to go with someone who can help you decide

(**That is**) _____ a good idea, he agreed (**I will**) _____ ask my brother if he can go

(**He is**) _____ working this week but maybe he can go on Saturday

I told my mate that (**he would**) _____ be glad to have someone with him

3. Put all the correct punctuation marks in this story.
   Fix the joined together sentences.

the first thing i do each day after i get up is to bring in the newspaper its a habit ive had for years it started when my father would ask me to get it for him jim he would call as soon as he woke up would you bring the paper in please he was as reliable as an alarm clock id always call back sure dad but secretly i would have liked to stay in bed a bit longer now that i have my own family i have thought about asking my son to get the paper for me but i guess i should wait until he can at least walk

Punctuation practice

1. **In this story, there are a lot of missing punctuation marks. Correct the story by putting in all the missing marks.**

when i got home from work i got my dogs leash and took her for a walk along the beach i saw my friend jim jogging towards me

hi julie he said

hi jim how are you I asked

im fine jim answered thats a nice dog what is his name

its not a male its a female I exclaimed

oh he was very embarrassed im sorry i got that wrong whats her name

her names lucy she had twelve puppies last week

wow thats a lot of puppies he said in surprise

youre right i agreed she needs some peace quiet and fresh air thats why ive brought her to the beach

id love to have one of the puppies do you have a spare to give to me jim inquired

no jim we dont i explained we are going to keep one and sell the rest

ok but could it come over and see them he requested

of course you can i told him ill be home all weekend

see you then said jim

bye i called as he jogged away

2. **In this story, there are a lot of missing punctuation marks, joined sentences and words that need apostrophes. Make all the corrections and rewrite the story on another page.**

my dog is named after an internet site when i first got her two years ago i did not know what name to give her and so she did not have a name for a few days then i noticed that she liked to lie by my feet when i was surfing the web and she barked at some of the things flashing on the screen and so i named her google and she has just had her first puppies and i was trying to think of names for them and when my boyfriend came over last night to see them he asked what are their names and i told him they do not have names yet and said why do not we try to think of some and then all of a sudden it hit me lets see if we can find some good names on the computer i laughed and he thought that would be fun and soon i had an idea why do not we call one puppy browser and he said that is a great name for the female and he said i have a good idea for the male puppy what is it i asked he said yahoo so those were the puppies names when i take them for a walk everyone laughs when i tell them their names

© 2009 Aber Publishing – Adult Skills   Punctuation - Book 1

Punctuation practice

Check your marks for No.1 on page 32 with story below.

When I got home from work, I got my dog's leash and took her for a walk along the beach.

I saw my friend Jim jogging towards me.

"Hi Julie," he said.

"Hi Jim, how are you?" I asked.

"I'm fine," Jim answered. "That's a nice dog. What is his name?"

"It's not a male, it's a female!" I exclaimed.

"Oh!" He was very embarrassed. "I'm sorry I got that wrong. What's her name?"

"Her name's Lucy," I told him. "She had twelve puppies last week!"

"Wow! That's a lot of puppies!" he said in surprise.

"You're right," I agreed. "She needs some peace, quiet and fresh air.
That's why I've brought her to the beach."

"I'd love to have one of the puppies. Do you have a spare to give to me?" Jim inquired.

"No, Jim, we don't," I explained. "We are going to keep one and sell the rest."

"OK, but could I come over and see them?" he requested.

"Of course you can," I told him. "I'll be home all weekend."

"See you then," said Jim.

"Bye," I called, as he jogged away.

Check your marks for No.2 on page 32 with story below.

My dog is named after an Internet site. When I first got her two years ago, I did not know what name to giver her. She didn't have a name for a few days. Then I noticed that she liked to lie by my feet when I was surfing the web. She barked at some of the things flashing on the screen. So I named her Google.

She has just had her first puppies. I was trying to think of names for them. When my boyfriend came over last night to see them he asked, "What are their names?"

I told him, "They don't have names yet. Why don't we try to think of some?"

All of a sudden it hit me. "Let's see if we can find some good names on the computer," I laughed. He thought that would be fun.

Soon I had an idea. "Why don't we call one puppy Browser?"

He said, "That is a great name for the female. I have a good idea for the male puppy."

"What is it?" I asked.

He said, "Yahoo." So those were the puppies' names.

When I take them for a walk, everyone laughs when I tell them their names.

© 2009 Aber Publishing – Adult Skills   Punctuation - Book 1